WE'RE RIGHT BEHIND YOU,
CHARLIE BROWN

Books by Charles M. Schulz

WE'RE RIGHT BEHIND YOU,
CHARLIE BROWN

A NEW PEANUTS BOOK

by Charles M. Schulz

HOLT, RINEHART AND WINSTON
New York · Chicago · San Francisco

Library of Congress Catalog Card Number: 63-20880

Published, January, 1964
Sixth Printing, September, 1967

87752-1514

Printed in the United States of America

WHATEVER HAPPENED TO THE GOOD OLD-FASHIONED NEIGHBORHOOD DOG?

I'M VERY PLEASED TO SEE SUCH A GOOD TURN-OUT...

WITH A LITTLE LUCK I THINK WE CAN HAVE A GOOD SEASON...

TODAY'S SPRING-TRAINING SESSION IS GOING TO BEGIN WITH A DEMONSTRATION...

LAST YEAR WE HIT INTO TOO MANY DOUBLE-PLAYS...

TWO OF OUR MEMBERS ARE GOING TO SHOW US HOW THIS CAN BE AVOIDED...

LINUS IS GOING TO BE THE SHORTSTOP AND SNOOPY IS GOING TO BE THE RUNNER GOING FROM FIRST TO SECOND WHO BREAKS UP THE DOUBLE-PLAY...

NOW, WATCH CAREFULLY.. THE PLAY BEGINS WITH LINUS FIELDING THE BALL, AND MAKING THE PLAY AT SECOND WHILE SNOOPY STREAKS TOWARD HIM..

AAUGH!!!

ARE THERE ANY QUESTIONS?

OH, GOOD GRIEF...HERE COMES CHARLIE BROWN..

I SUPPOSE HE'LL WANT ME TO PLAY BALL...''I'LL THROW THE BALL, SNOOPY, AND YOU CHASE IT!'' PHOOEY!!!

?

SNOOPY?

?

I GUESS HE'S NOT AROUND.. I JUST WANTED TO TELL HIM THAT SUPPER WAS READY..

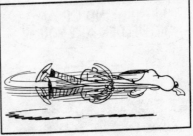

DON'T ASK ME TO EXPLAIN...
JUST GO GET A SHOVEL !!

FIVE O'CLOCK...TIME TO FEED THE DOG..

OKAY, SNOOPY... HERE YOU ARE...

OH, IT'S SUPPERTIME! IT'S SUPPERTIME!

SUPPERTIME! SUPPERTIME! SUPPERTIME!!

HEY! CUT IT OUT NOW! WATCH WHAT YOU'RE DOING!

OH, IT'S SUPPERTIME! IT'S SUPPERTIME!!

YES, IT'S SUPPERTIME!

OH, YES, YES, YES, YES, IT'S SUPPERTIME! IT'S SUPPERTIME! IT'S...

ALL RIGHT, EAT!

GOOD GRIEF!

SO WHAT'S WRONG WITH MAKING MEALTIME A JOYOUS OCCASION?

SCHULZ

PTUI!

PTUI!

UNTIL IT IS DEMONSTRATED, ONE FORGETS THE REALLY GREAT DIFFERENCE THAT EXISTS BETWEEN THE MERELY COMPETENT AMATEUR AND THE VERY EXPERT PROFESSIONAL

EXCUSE ME...

CLOMP!

THANK YOU VERY MUCH..

THINK NOTHING OF IT...YOU'LL HEAR FROM THE HUMANE SOCIETY FIRST THING IN THE MORNING!

HEY, WAKE UP...IT'S ALMOST THERE!

WHAM!

FOR A SEVEN-TEN SPLIT HE WAKES ME UP!

ONLY THREE MORE DAYS AND THE "GREAT PUMPKIN" WILL APPEAR..

TIME FLIES...

SO DOES THE "GREAT PUMPKIN"

EACH YEAR THE "GREAT PUMPKIN" RISES OUT OF A PUMPKIN PATCH, AND FLIES THROUGH THE AIR WITH HIS BAG OF TOYS!

ACCORDING TO YOUR BROTHER, LINUS

OH, BUT I BELIEVE HIM! I REALLY DO!

AND THIS YEAR I'VE STARTED MY OWN PUMPKIN PATCH...I'M HOPING THAT THIS YEAR THE "GREAT PUMPKIN" WILL SELECT MINE AS BEING THE MOST SINCERE!

THE WHOLE THING IS RIDICULOUS..

OF COURSE IT IS, BUT IT'S WORTH THE GAMBLE...IF HE SELECTS MY PUMPKIN PATCH, I'LL BE FAMOUS!

JUST THINK WHAT IT WOULD BE WORTH IN ADVERTISING ENDORSEMENTS ALONE! I'D BE RICH!!

IS THIS YOUR PUMPKIN PATCH, LUCY?

YES, DO YOU THINK I HAVE A CHANCE?

WELL?

THIS IS THE MOST HYPOCRITICAL PUMPKIN PATCH I HAVE EVER SEEN!

SIGH

HALLOWEEN PUMPKINS 50¢

IT'S KIND OF COLD TONIGHT...IT SHOULDN'T BE SO COLD THIS TIME OF YEAR...

I WONDER IF SNOOPY IS WARM ENOUGH...

I THINK I'LL TAKE MY SLEEPING BAG OUT TO HIM..

IF A PERSON IS GOING TO OWN A DOG, HE MUST LEARN TO ASSUME THE OBLIGATIONS OF THAT OWNERSHIP!

I'M GLAD I TOOK IT OUT TO HIM..HE SEEMED TO APPRECIATE IT..

I CAN SLEEP BETTER MYSELF NOW, KNOWING THAT HE'S WARM..

A SAIL ON THE HORIZON, SIR!

HERE'S THE CAPTAIN OF HIS MAJESTY'S SHIP STANDING BRAVELY AT THE BOW...

"WE CAN'T BE SURE IT'S A PIRATE SHIP, BOYS...WAIT UNTIL SHE FIRES THE FIRST SHOT...THEN MOVE IN FOR THE KILL!"

BOOM!

WE'RE HIT!!

SWIM FOR YOUR LIVES, BOYS! EVERY MAN FOR HIMSELF!

BLACKBEARD IS STILL THE TERROR OF THE HIGH SEAS!

THERE'S NEVER ANYTHING TO DO!

I NEED SOMETHING TO CHALLENGE ME.. I NEED SOME NEW INTEREST...

IF YOU WANT A HOBBY, WHY DON'T YOU COLLECT LEAVES? YOU CAN PRESS THEM BETWEEN THE PAGES OF A BOOK..

THAT'S A WONDERFUL IDEA!

WHAP!

WELL, I DID IT! I'VE COLLECTED OVER A DOZEN DIFFERENT KINDS OF LEAVES!

MY ONLY PROBLEM CAME IN SELECTING WHAT SORT OF BOOK I SHOULD PRESS THEM IN..OF COURSE, I KNEW IT HAD TO BE A LARGE VOLUME...

I FIRST THOUGHT OF "THE DECLINE AND FALL OF THE ROMAN EMPIRE," AND THEN I CONSIDERED "LOOK HOMEWARD ANGEL," BUT I FINALLY DECIDED ON A VOLUME CALLED, "THE PROPHECIES OF DANIEL" BECAUSE I FELT THAT..

GET OUT OF HERE!

PEOPLE REALLY AREN'T INTERESTED IN HEARING YOU TALK ABOUT YOUR HOBBY..

YOU NEVER KNOW IN WHICH PART OF THE COUNTRY IT WILL HAPPEN..

ON HALLOWEEN NIGHT IN 1959 THE GREAT PUMPKIN APPEARED IN THE PUMPKIN PATCH OF BOOTS RUTMAN OF CONNECTICUT..

IF YOU DON'T BELIEVE ME, LOOK IN THE RECORD!

IN 1960 THE GREAT PUMPKIN APPEARED IN THE PUMPKIN PATCH OF R.W. DANIELS OF TEXAS...

AGAIN I SAY, IF YOU DON'T BELIEVE ME, LOOK IN THE RECORD!

NOW, SOMEWHERE IN THIS WORLD THE GREAT PUMPKIN HAS TO APPEAR THIS HALLOWEEN NIGHT!

WHY NOT HERE?!

MAYBE THIS PUMPKIN PATCH ISN'T BIG ENOUGH?

SIZE HAS NOTHING TO DO WITH IT! IT'S SINCERITY THAT COUNTS! ASK BOOTS RUTMAN! ASK R.W. DANIELS!

MAYBE IT'S NEATNESS, TOO...MAYBE HE APPEARS IN THE PUMPKIN PATCH THAT HAS THE LEAST WEEDS

NO, NO, NO, NO, NO, NO, NO! IT'S SINCERITY THAT COUNTS! THE GREAT PUMPKIN WILL APPEAR IN WHICHEVER PUMPKIN PATCH HE DECIDES IS THE MOST SINCERE!!

I'D HATE TO HAVE TO MAKE SUCH A DECISION!

OH, NO!

THIS IS "SHOW AND TELL" DAY AT SCHOOL, ISN'T IT? RATS! I FORGOT TO BRING SOMETHING...

DID YOU REMEMBER THAT THIS WAS "SHOW AND TELL" DAY, LINUS?

YES, I HAVE A COUPLE OF THINGS HERE TO SHOW THE CLASS...

THESE ARE COPIES I'VE BEEN MAKING OF SOME OF THE DEAD SEA SCROLLS...

SEE? THIS IS A DUPLICATE OF A SCROLL OF ISAIAH, CHAPTERS 38 TO 40...IT WAS MADE FROM SEVENTEEN PIECES OF SHEEPSKIN, AND WAS FOUND IN A CAVE BY A SHEPHERD...

HERE I'VE MADE A COPY OF THE EARLIEST KNOWN FRAGMENT EVER FOUND...IT'S A PORTION OF I SAMUEL 23:9-16...I'LL TRY TO EXPLAIN TO THE CLASS HOW THESE MANUSCRIPTS HAVE INFLUENCED MODERN SCHOLARS...

VERY INTERESTING..

I THOUGHT IT MIGHT BE AT LEAST FAINTLY APPROPRIATE TO THE SEASON..

ARE YOU BRINGING SOMETHING FOR "SHOW AND TELL", CHARLIE BROWN?

WELL, I HAD A LITTLE RED FIRE ENGINE HERE, BUT I THINK MAYBE I'LL JUST FORGET IT..

SCHULZ

AH! A PERFECT DAY!

ALL RIGHT, RISE AN' SHINE! IT'S RABBIT-CHASING TIME!!

OH, GOOD GRIEF!

THE SNOW IS FRESH AND THE AIR IS CLEAR...I PREDICT WE'LL SEE LOTS OF GAME!

HOW CAN YOU CHASE RABBITS IN THE MIDDLE OF THE NIGHT?

WE'LL START HERE...THIS IS A BIG FIELD, AND YOU SHOULD BE ABLE TO PICK UP THE SCENT WITHOUT...

WAKE UP!

OKAY! HERE WE GO!!

SNIF SNIF SNIF SNIF

SNIF SNIF SNIF SNIF SNIF

I GUESS WE'RE NOT GOING TO FIND ANY SNOOPY, BUT AT LEAST WE TRIED...

EVEN THOUGH YOU'VE FAILED, IT ALWAYS MAKES YOU FEEL BETTER WHEN YOU KNOW YOU'VE DONE YOUR BEST!

I'D HATE TO DISILLUSION HER, BUT I DON'T EVEN KNOW WHAT A RABBIT SMELLS LIKE!

SCHULZ

OH, NO! DON'T TELL ME! NOT AGAIN!

HERE'S YOUR PIECE FOR THE CHRISTMAS PROGRAM..

"SO THE WORDS SPOKEN THROUGH JEREMIAH THE PROPHET WERE FULFILLED: 'A VOICE WAS HEARD IN RAMA, WAILING AND LOUD LAMENTS; IT WAS RACHEL WEEPING FOR HER CHILDREN, AND REFUSING ALL CONSOLATION BECAUSE THEY WERE NO MORE.'" GOOD GRIEF!!

MEMORIZE IT, AND BE READY TO RECITE IT BY NEXT SUNDAY!

I CAN'T MEMORIZE SOMETHING LIKE THIS IN A **WEEK**! THIS IS GOING TO TAKE **RESEARCH**

WHO WAS JEREMIAH? WHERE WAS RAMA? WHY WAS RACHEL SO UPSET?

YOU CAN'T RECITE SOMETHING UNTIL YOU KNOW THE "WHO," THE "WHERE" AND THE "WHY"!

I'LL TELL YOU THE "WHO", THE "WHERE" AND THE "WHY"!

YOU START MEMORIZING RIGHT NOW, OR YOU'LL KNOW **WHO** IS GOING TO SLUG YOU, AND YOU'LL KNOW **WHERE** SHE'S GOING TO SLUG YOU AND YOU'LL KNOW **WHY** SHE SLUGGED YOU!!!

CHRISTMAS IS NOT ONLY GETTING TOO COMMERCIAL, IT'S GETTING TOO DANGEROUS!

SIGH!

I DON'T THINK I'D MIND SCHOOL AT ALL IF IT WEREN'T FOR THESE LUNCH HOURS...I GUESS I'LL SIT ON THIS BENCH...

I HAVE TO SIT BY MYSELF BECAUSE NOBODY ELSE EVER INVITES ME TO SIT WITH THEM...

PEANUT BUTTER AGAIN! OH, WELL, MOM DOES HER BEST...

THOSE KIDS LOOK LIKE THEY'RE HAVING A LOT OF FUN...I WISH THEY LIKED ME... NOBODY LIKES ME...

THE PTA DID A GOOD JOB PAINTING THESE BENCHES...

I'D GIVE ANYTHING IN THE WORLD IF THAT LITTLE GIRL WITH THE RED HAIR WOULD COME OVER, AND SIT WITH ME...

I GET TIRED OF ALWAYS BEING ALONE...I WISH THE BELL WOULD RING...

A BANANA...RATS! MOM ALWAYS...STILL, I GUESS SHE MEANS WELL...

I BET I COULD RUN JUST AS FAST AS THOSE KIDS. THAT'S A GOOD GAME THEY'RE PLAYING...

THAT LITTLE GIRL WITH THE RED HAIR IS A GOOD RUNNER...

AH, THERE'S THE BELL! ONE MORE LUNCH HOUR OUT OF THE WAY...

TWO-THOUSAND, ONE-HUNDRED AND TWENTY TO GO!

SCHULZ

I GOT IT!

YOU GIMME BACK MY BLANKET!

NO! I'VE GOT IT, AND I'M GOING TO KEEP IT! THIS IS THE START YOU NEED TO BREAK THE HABIT!

APPARENTLY YOU HAVEN'T READ THE LATEST SCIENTIFIC REPORTS..

A BLANKET IS AS IMPORTANT TO A CHILD AS A HOBBY IS TO AN ADULT..

MANY A MAN SPENDS HIS TIME RESTORING ANTIQUE AUTOMOBILES OR BUILDING MODEL TRAINS OR COLLECTING OLD TELEPHONES OR EVEN STUDYING ABOUT THE CIVIL WAR...THIS IS CALLED, "PLAYING WITH THE PAST"

REALLY?

CERTAINLY!!! AND THIS IS GOOD FOR IT HELPS THESE MEN TO COPE WITH THEIR EVERYDAY PROBLEMS...

NOW, I FEEL THAT IT IS ABSOLUTELY NECESSARY FOR ME TO GET MY BLANKET BACK SO I'M JUST GOING TO GIVE IT A GOOD...

..YANK!

IT'S SURPRISING WHAT YOU CAN ACCOMPLISH WITH A LITTLE SMOOTH TALKING AND SOME FAST ACTION!

SCHULZ

SCHULZ

SMACK!
ZIP!

TRICKED! TRICKED BY A BABY AND A STUPID DOG!

SHE KISSES ME, AND HE GRABS THE BLANKET! I CAN'T STAND IT!

THE MORE I THINK ABOUT IT, THE MADDER I GET!

WHO DID YOU SAY WAS HERE? DR. SPOCK? IN PERSON?

YOU SAY DR. SPOCK IS HERE IN PERSON JUST TO SEE US?

DID YOU SAY DR. SPOCK IS RIGHT HERE AT OUR FRONT DOOR? IN PERSON?

AND THAT NICE MAN FROM THE HUMANE SOCIETY? YOU SAY HE'S HERE, TOO?!

AAUGH!

HOW DOES HE **KNOW**? HOW DOES HE **DO** IT?!!!

HOW DID HE KNOW I HAD A COOKIE IN MY POCKET WHEN I WENT BY HIM THE SECOND TIME?

HE LISTENS TO YOUR FOOTSTEPS... WITH THE COOKIE IN YOUR POCKET, YOU **WEIGHED** MORE!

THE ONLY WAY YOU CAN SURVIVE THESE DAYS IS TO KEEP YOUR EAR TO THE GROUND!

RATS! THERE GOES THE BELL..

I CAN'T STAND IT!

OH, HOW I HATE THESE LUNCH HOURS!

I ALWAYS HAVE TO EAT ALONE BECAUSE NOBODY LIKES ME..

PEANUT BUTTER AGAIN..

I WISH THAT LITTLE RED-HAIRED GIRL WOULD COME OVER, AND SIT WITH ME...

WOULDN'T IT BE GREAT IF SHE'D WALK OVER HERE, AND SAY, "MAY I EAT LUNCH WITH YOU, CHARLIE BROWN?"

I'D GIVE ANYTHING TO TALK WITH HER...SHE'D NEVER LIKE ME, THOUGH...I'M SO BLAH AND SO STUPID... SHE'D NEVER LIKE ME...

I WONDER WHAT WOULD HAPPEN IF I WENT OVER AND TRIED TO TALK TO HER! EVERYBODY WOULD PROBABLY LAUGH... SHE'D PROBABLY BE INSULTED, TOO, IF SOMEONE AS BLAH AS I AM TRIED TO TALK TO HER

I HATE LUNCH HOUR..ALL IT DOES IS MAKE ME LONELY...DURING CLASS IT DOESN'T MATTER....

I CAN'T EVEN EAT... NOTHING TASTES GOOD...

WHY CAN'T I EAT LUNCH WITH THAT LITTLE RED-HAIRED GIRL? THEN I'D BE HAPPY...

RATS! NOBODY IS EVER GOING TO LIKE ME..

LUNCH HOUR IS THE LONELIEST HOUR OF THE DAY'!

I IMAGINE THAT EVEN AN INEXPENSIVE FIELDER'S GLOVE WOULD LAST A PLAYER LIKE HIM FOR YEARS!

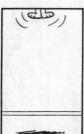

I THINK YOU'D ENJOY READING IT..

MAYBE SALLY WOULD RUN IN, AND GET IT...

SALLY, WILL YOU GO BACK IN THE HOUSE FOR ME, PLEASE, AND GET THAT NEW COMIC BOOK?

GO GET IT YOURSELF! I'M NOT YOUR SERVANT!

BOY, YOU SURE DON'T HAVE YOUR LITTLE SISTER TRAINED RIGHT, CHARLIE BROWN...

WHY, SHE SHOULD BE DOING ANYTHING YOU TELL HER!

YOU'VE GOT TO HAVE CONTROL, CHARLIE BROWN...COMPLETE AND ABSOLUTE CONTROL!

YOU SHOULD BE ABLE TO MAKE HER DANCE LIKE A MARIONETTE ON STRINGS...

TAKE ME FOR EXAMPLE... I PLAY LINUS AS A PIANIST PLAYS A CONCERT GRAND!

IS THAT TRUE?

THE EARLY MORNING LIGHT REVEALS A VULTURE PERCHED HIGH ON THE LIMB OF A TREE

AH! A VICTIM!

THE VULTURE PEERS...

HE SWOOPS!

BONG!

RATS! HOW HUMILIATING!

A GOOD VULTURE HATES TO ACCEPT CHARITY!

I SUPPOSE IF I TOLD YOU THERE'S A VULTURE OUTSIDE THAT'S BOTHERING ME, YOU'D SAY I WAS CRAZY, WOULDN'T YOU?

YES, I WOULD!

WHAT HAPPENED TO YOUR VULTURE?

HE'S NOT BOTHERING ME ANY MORE...HE GOT TREE SICK!

SCHULZ

FORGET IT.... IT WAS A HOME RUN!

CAN I HELP IT IF MY HOUSE FACES THE BALL PARK?

ONE FINGER WILL MEAN A FAST BALL, TWO FINGERS A CURVE AND THREE FINGERS A SLOW BALL...OKAY?

FINE

WHAT WERE YOU TWO TALKING ABOUT?

WE WERE JUST DISCUSSING OUR SIGNALS

OH..

I THOUGHT MAYBE YOU WERE TALKING ABOUT **ME**...

I GUESS THAT'S UNDERSTANDABLE IF YOU'RE PARTICULARLY SENSITIVE!

WHAT'S THIS?

OH, IT'S JUST A LITTLE PICTURE I DREW OF A MAN ON A HORSE...

OH, I JUST LOVE HORSE PICTURES!

COULD I HAVE IT, CHARLIE BROWN? COULD I HAVE IT TO HANG ON MY WALL?

WELL, I GUESS SO... IF YOU THINK IT'S GOOD ENOUGH...I MEAN..

AND HOW ABOUT SIGNING IT? WILL YOU SIGN IT, TOO? WILL YOU PUT YOUR NAME ON IT?

ALL RIGHT..WHAT DO YOU WANT ME TO DO...JUST SIGN MY NAME, OR...

YOU WERE GOING TO DO IT, WEREN'T YOU?

HA!HA!HA!HA! HA!HA!HA!HA!

YOU REALLY THOUGHT I WANTED TO HANG THIS STUPID PICTURE ON MY WALL, DIDN'T YOU? HA!HA!HA!HA!

..AND HE EVEN THOUGHT I WANTED HIM TO SIGN IT! HA!HA!HA!HA!

I CAN'T STAND IT!

SCHULZ

"WHEN SHE SAW THE LITTLE HOUSE IN THE WOODS, SHE WONDERED WHO LIVED THERE SO SHE KNOCKED AT THE DOOR. NO ONE ANSWERED SO SHE KNOCKED AGAIN."

WHAT DO YOU THINK WILL HAPPEN?

I CAN'T IMAGINE

"...STILL NO ONE ANSWERED, SO GOLDILOCKS OPENED THE DOOR AND WALKED IN. THERE BEFORE HER, IN THE LITTLE ROOM, SHE SAW A TABLE SET FOR THREE..."

"THERE WAS A GREAT BIG BOWL OF PORRIDGE, A MIDDLE-SIZED BOWL OF PORRIDGE, AND A LITTLE, WEE BOWL OF PORRIDGE. SHE TASTED THE GREAT BIG BOWL OF PORRIDGE..."

"'OH, THIS IS TOO HOT,' SHE SAID. THEN SHE TASTED THE MIDDLE-SIZED BOWL OF PORRIDGE. 'OH, THIS IS TOO COLD.' THEN SHE TASTED THE LITTLE, WEE BOWL. 'OH, THIS IS JUST RIGHT,' SHE SAID, AND SHE ATE IT ALL UP.'"

I HAVE A QUESTION!

ABOUT WHAT?

WELL, IT'S IN REGARD TO COOLING...IT WOULD SEEM TO ME THAT IF THE MIDDLE-SIZED BOWL WAS COLD, THE LITTLE, WEE BOWL WOULD BE COLD, TOO, RATHER THAN 'JUST RIGHT', AND..

POW!

I NEVER EVEN BROUGHT UP THE FAR MORE OBVIOUS POINT OF UNLAWFUL ENTRY!

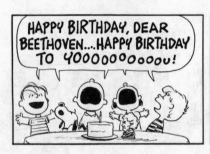

HOLD STILL!

HOLD STILL, I SAY!

IS THIS A SCHOOL PROJECT, LUCY?

OF COURSE, IT IS, YOU BLOCKHEAD! WHY ELSE WOULD I BE CHASING A BUNCH OF STUPID BUTTERFLIES?!

HERE... I THINK MAYBE YOUR TEACHER WILL LIKE THESE..

PROMISE YOU'LL LET THEM GO AFTER YOU'VE STUDIED THEM, WILL YOU?

I JUST CAN'T BELIEVE THAT RACHEL CARSON WOULD EVER LET HERSELF GET SO UPSET!

EMPTY! AND I'M DYING OF THIRST!

THAT'S ONE I'M GOING TO HAVE TO THINK ABOUT FOR AWHILE!

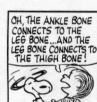

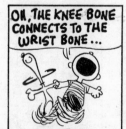

ZIP!

SCHULZ

THUS ENDETH THE DIVING CAREER!

HERE IT IS... THREE O'CLOCK... "DOCTORS' ROUND TABLE"

WHAT ARE YOU WATCHING?

"MONSTER MADNESS"

I DON'T SUPPOSE YOU'D CARE TO WATCH "DOCTORS' ROUND TABLE"?

NO, I WOULDN'T!

THEY HAVE A GOOD PANEL TODAY.. A PHYSICIAN, A PHILOSOPHER, A THEOLOGIAN AND A DENTIST...

THEY'RE DISCUSSING, "WHERE CAIN GOT HIS WIFE AND THE IMPORTANCE OF A PRE-SCHOOL CHECK-UP"...

WELL, YOU MIGHT AS WELL FORGET IT BECAUSE **I'M** WATCHING "MONSTER MADNESS"!

I'LL GO OVER TO CHARLIE BROWN'S HOUSE...MAYBE HE'LL LET ME WATCH MY PROGRAM OVER THERE

HI, LINUS...COME ON IN...YOU JUST MISSED "DOCTORS' ROUND TABLE"

IT WAS PRETTY GOOD.... THE PHILOSOPHER AND THE THEOLOGIAN AGREED THAT A PRE-SCHOOL CHECK-UP IS A VERY WISE ACTION...

WHERE HAVE **YOU** BEEN? YOU MISSED A REAL GOOD PROGRAM...

THE PHYSICIAN AND THE DENTIST GOT INTO A BIG FIGHT OVER WHERE CAIN GOT HIS WIFE!

SCHULZ

IT'S A STORY I'VE BEEN READING CALLED "THE PIT AND THE PENDULUM" BY POE, AND IT'S ABOUT THIS MAN, SEE, WHO IS A PRISONER....

HE'S TIED TO A TABLE, AND THIS BIG PENDULUM KEEPS SWINGING BACK AND FORTH ABOVE HIM, GETTING NEARER AND NEARER...

IT SOUNDS LIKE AN EXCITING STORY.. I'LL HAVE TO READ IT..

I THINK YOU'D ENJOY IT.. I REALLY DO...

THAT EDGAR ALLAN POE WAS A RIOT..

GOOD GRIEF!

THIS IS GETTING RIDICULOUS!

ANOTHER WEEK HAS GONE BY AND THIS GRASS STILL HASN'T BEEN CUT! PRETTY SOON I WON'T EVEN BE ABLE TO SEE!

CHARLIE BROWN, WHAT'S THE MATTER WITH YOU?

THAT GRASS AROUND SNOOPY'S DOGHOUSE IS GETTING SO TALL IT LOOKS LIKE A **JUNGLE!**

WHY DON'T YOU **DO** SOMETHING ABOUT IT? WHAT'S THE MATTER WITH YOU? WHY DON'T YOU CUT IT? WHY DON'T...

ALL RIGHT! ALL RIGHT! I'LL GO GET A LAWN MOWER!

DON'T BOTHER...I THINK HE'S SOLVED THE PROBLEM HIMSELF....

CHOMP CHOMP CHOMP CHOMP CHOMP CHOMP

SCHULZ

YOU KNOW WHAT?

WHAT?

FALLING STARS DON'T SCREAM!

LET'S GO OVER ON MY FRONT SIDEWALK...WE'LL HAVE MORE ROOM...

WHAT ABOUT LUCY? SHE'S JUMPING ROPE RIGHT THERE..

SHE'LL JUST HAVE TO MOVE, THAT'S ALL..

OKAY, THROW IT ALL THE WAY!

WHAT DO YOU THINK **YOU'RE** DOING?

CHARLIE BROWN AND I ARE GOING TO PLAY A LITTLE CATCH

NOT WHERE I'M JUMPING ROPE, YOU'RE NOT! NOW, GET OUT OF HERE!

WHY SHOULD I? I LIVE HERE, TOO, YOU KNOW!

WHY SHOULD **YOU** ALWAYS HAVE **YOUR** WAY? WHAT MAKES YOU THINK **YOU'RE** SO IMPORTANT? WHY SHOULD **I** ALWAYS DO WHAT **YOU** SAY?

WHAT COULD I DO? SUDDENLY I WAS LOOKING DOWN THE BARREL OF A FIST!

I'M SORT OF A FANATIC ABOUT SAVING THINGS...

YOU'VE NEVER SEEN MY LEAF COLLECTION, HAVE YOU, CHARLIE BROWN?

I'D LIKE YOU TO SEE IT...I'VE GOT HUNDREDS OF THEM, AND THEY'RE ALL MOUNTED IN BOOKS AND LABELED AND EVERYTHING...

I HAVE A BLACK WILLOW, A BUR OAK, A SHAGBARK HICKORY, A GINKGO, A QUAKING ASPEN AND A WHITE ASH...

EVERY TIME OUR FAMILY GOES ON A TRIP, I BRING HOME SOME NEW LEAVES...IF THERE'S ONE THING I'M REALLY PROUD OF, IT'S... ..

GANGWAY!!

YAHOO!!

..MY. LEAF COLLECTION!

SCHULZ

THIS IS THE BIG DAY!

NINE HUNDRED AND NINETY NINE DAYS! ONE TO GO...THIS IS IT!

LUCY, MAY I READ YOUR NEW COMIC BOOK?

NO, YOU CAN'T! AND STOP BOTHERING ME!

YOU DID IT! YOU DID IT!

MY HEARTIEST CONGRATULATIONS! YOU DID IT!!

?

YOU HAVE BEEN **CRABBY** FOR ONE THOUSAND DAYS IN A ROW! YOU HAVE JUST SET AN ALL-TIME RECORD! I **KNEW** YOU COULD DO IT!

SEE? I'VE BEEN KEEPING TRACK ON THIS CALENDAR SINCE TUESDAY, DEC. 9th 1959! REMEMBER THAT DAY?

YOU THREW AN APPLE CORE AT ME! SINCE THEN YOU HAVE GONE ONE THOUSAND DAYS WITHOUT FAILING ONCE TO BE CRABBY!

LET ME SHAKE YOUR HAND AGAIN!

I'D ALSO LIKE TO PRESENT YOU WITH THIS SPECIALLY INSCRIBED SCROLL COMMEMORATING THIS HISTORICAL EVENT...

AGAIN MAY I SAY, "CONGRATULATIONS!" YOU ARE AN INSPIRATION TO ALL THE CRABBY PEOPLE IN THIS WORLD!

ONE RARELY GETS A CHANCE TO SEE SUCH CAREFULLY PREPARED SARCASM!

CHARLIE BROWN, YOU CAN'T POSSIBLY IMAGINE HOW GLAD WE'LL ALL BE WHEN THE KITE-FLYING SEASON IS OVER!

HOW ABOUT RIGHT FIELD? WHERE'S LUCY?

I'M ON MY WAY, CHARLIE BROWN...START THE GAME!

WHAT IN THE WORLD ARE YOU CARRYING IN YOUR GLOVE?

CRACKER SANDWICHES! YOU DON'T EXPECT ME TO STAND OUT THERE IN RIGHT FIELD AND **STARVE** TO DEATH, DO YOU?!

THERE'S NOTHING BETTER THAN TWO CRACKERS WITH BUTTER AND HONEY BETWEEN THEM

CHOMP CHOMP CHOMP MANAGERS JUST DON'T REALIZE THE PROBLEMS WE OUTFIELDERS FACE

CHOMP CHOMP CHOMP THEY DON'T REALIZE HOW BORING IT GETS OUT HERE WHEN NOBODY HITS THE..

OH, OH!

CRUNCH

UGH! WHAT A MESS!

HERE Y'GO, CHARLIE BROWN! COMIN' HOME!

I CAN'T STAND IT! I JUST CAN'T STAND IT!

CHARLIE BROWN, I'VE BEEN FEELING AWFULLY GUILTY ABOUT NOT GIVING YOU A VALENTINE THIS YEAR...I'D LIKE FOR YOU TO HAVE THIS ONE

HOLD ON THERE! WHAT DO YOU THINK YOU'RE DOING? WHO DO YOU THINK YOU ARE?!

WHERE WERE YOU FEBRUARY 14th WHEN EVERYONE ELSE WAS GIVING OUT VALENTINES? IS KINDNESS AND THOUGHTFULNESS SOMETHING YOU CAN MAKE RETROACTIVE? DON'T YOU THINK HE HAS ANY FEELINGS?!

YOU AND YOUR FRIENDS ARE THE MOST THOUGHTLESS BUNCH I'VE EVER KNOWN! YOU DON'T CARE ANYTHING ABOUT CHARLIE BROWN! YOU JUST HATE TO FEEL GUILTY!

AND NOW YOU HAVE THE NERVE TO COME AROUND A WHOLE MONTH LATER, AND OFFER HIM A USED VALENTINE JUST TO EASE YOUR CONSCIENCE! WELL LET ME TELL YOU SOMETHING... CHARLIE BROWN DOESN'T NEED YOUR...

DON'T INTERFERE...I'LL TAKE IT!

I'VE BEEN DOING A LITTLE THINKING..

YOU KNOW... SORT OF MULLING THINGS OVER..

AND I FEEL THAT AS LONG AS WE HAVE TO LIVE TOGETHER IN THE SAME FAMILY, WE SHOULD TRY TO GET ALONG...

I JUST THINK WE COULD WORK A LITTLE HARDER AT IT, THAT'S ALL...

DO YOU AGREE?

AND I FEEL THAT AS LONG AS WE HAVE TO LIVE TOGETHER IN THE SAME FAMILY, WE SHOULD TRY TO GET ALONG...

I JUST THINK WE COULD WORK A LITTLE HARDER AT IT, THAT'S ALL...DO YOU AGREE?

YOU'RE RIGHT... TALKING TO LUCY IS LIKE TALKING TO A BRICK WALL!

SIT UP, SNOOPY, AND I'LL GIVE YOU A NICE PIECE OF CANDY...

HUMPF!

"SIT UP, SNOOPY, AND I'LL GIVE YOU A NICE PIECE OF CANDY"....PHOOEY! WHO NEEDS IT?!

I GET SICK AND TIRED OF THEIR CONDESCENDING ATTITUDE!

WHY SHOULD I HAVE TO BEG FOR EVERYTHING? I'M AS GOOD AS THEY ARE! I DON'T NEED THEM! I CAN GET ALONG BY MYSELF!

OR CAN I?

WHERE IN THE WORLD ARE YOU GOING?

I'M GOING TO SPEND THE NIGHT AT CHARLIE BROWN'S HOUSE..

DO YOU EVER HAVE PROWLERS AROUND HERE, CHARLIE BROWN?

WHY? ARE YOU SCARED?

OH, I'M ALWAYS SORT OF WORRIED ABOUT PROWLERS...

YOU FORGET THAT WE HAVE A WATCHDOG HERE...

YOU MEAN SNOOPY? IS HE A GOOD WATCHDOG?

I DON'T THINK THERE'S A BETTER ONE..

YOU'RE RIGHT...SEEING HIM OUT THERE ON GUARD MAKES ME FEEL A LOT BETTER!